Sam's Sister

by Juliet C. Bond

Illustrated by Dawn W. Majewski

Perspectives Press, Inc.

Indianapolis, Indiana

To Jacob and Lilly and to mothers and children everywhere, birth or otherwise,

as we try to navigate and enjoy this colorful world...

"Y por eso los grandes amores de muchos colores me gustan a mi"

"And that's why I love this colorful world so much..."

Juliet C. Bond

Perspectives Press, Inc.
P.O. Box 90318
Indianapolis, IN 46290-0318 USA
(317)872-3055
www.perspectivespress.com

Cover and interior design by Bookwrights
Manufactured in China
ISBN 0-944934-30-7

Library of Congress Cataloging-in-Publication Data

Bond, Juliet C.
    Sam's sister / by Juliet C. Bond; illustrated Dawn W. Majewski
        p. cm.
    Summary: Five-year-old Rosa becomes a big sister to a baby boy for whom their mother plans an open adoption because she cannot properly care for another child.
        ISBN 0-944934-30-7
    [J. Adoption—Fiction. 2. Brothers and sisters—Fiction. 3. Family—Fiction.] I. Majewski, Dawn, ill. II.Title.

PZ7 B63672Sam 2004
[E]—dc22

2003060916

When I was five, something very special happened.

At first, I was worried. I guessed Mommy was thinking hard about something. She stopped singing. She forgot to smile. She was quiet.

I was sure something was on her mind when I was singing our favorite song, *De Colores*, and my mommy got mad. She said, "Stop being so loud Rosa!"

I worried that Mommy was sick. Maybe she didn't love me anymore.

"Mommy," I said, "What is wrong?"

Mommy sat me on her lap and said, "Rosa, Mommy has been very worried about something and you should know what it is."

She smiled at me, but her eyes looked sad.

"There is a new baby growing in my tummy, but when he's born, I can't take care of him. We don't have enough room here. We don't have a crib or special baby food or even a stroller to push the baby in. There won't be anyone to care for the baby when I go to work and you're at school.

"Rosa, babies need energy and lots of attention. Right now I couldn't provide those things for *two* children, even with your help."

Mommy said, "I might know what to do. There is a family I have met who want a baby to love. They are hoping we will let them help us take care of the baby in my tummy."

"Will they take me too?" I asked.

"No way, José!" she said and hugged me tight. "We have just what we need to take care of each other and you will always live with me. I love you very, very much."

"Do you love the baby in your tummy?" I asked.

"Yes, we will love him, too. He just won't live with us."

Soon Mommy's tummy grew big. I had lots of questions.

"Will I be the baby's sister?" I asked, because sometimes I wanted the baby to stay with us.

My mommy said, "Even though he won't live here, you will always be the baby's big sister, Rosa."

Then, one day, we went to a restaurant to meet the baby's mommy and daddy. I wasn't sure I would like them, but they were very nice.

The mommy's name was Sarah and she had a pretty smile. Joe, the daddy,

liked to laugh real loud. He brought me a coloring book without any pictures in it. He asked, "Would you make pictures and stories for the baby?"

I nodded. I liked that I had a way to tell the baby I love him too.

On the day my brother was born, I had a sleepover at Aunt Maria's and, in the morning, she brought me to the hospital. Joe and Sarah were already there.

Sarah said, "The baby's name is going to be Sam."

Joe said, "I hope you and your mommy can pick out a middle name for Sam."

In mommy's special room, I met Sam. I was very excited!

"Mommy, Mommy," I called and climbed onto the bed with her. "We get to pick a middle name for Sam."

After trying out many names, we decided on *Querido* because it means *wanted* in Spanish. "Sam should always know he was wanted," said Mommy. "He was wanted by us, and by Sarah and Joe."

That night, Mommy came home
with me and Sam went home
with Sarah and Joe.

Sarah and Joe had given Mommy a letter for us to read. We waited until we were both tucked into Mommy's bed and then we read the letter that promised to take such good care of Sam.

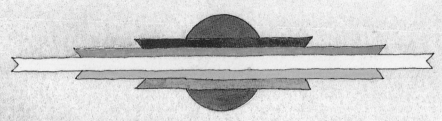

Dear Laura and Rosa,

We are overwhelmed by the trust you have placed in Sarah and me. Our long awaited dream of becoming parents has finally come true.

We know that this was not an easy decision for you and that you might sometimes feel very sad. We know that you suffered for our happiness. But never forget that you are the bearers of joy.

You will always be an important part of Sam's life. The power of Sam's growing life before birth, the reason for his freckles and crooked smile; these are things only you can tell him about.

We will always love and care for Sam. We will sing to him, read to him, and take him on walks to the park and on vacations with our families. We will hold him when he skins his knees and dry his tears when he cries. He will be our world.

We will thank you every day for making us Sam's parents.

Love,

Joe and Sarah

Mommy and I cried while we read that letter. Later that night, I had a nightmare and needed to stay with Mommy in her bed. Mommy told me we would talk to a counselor about missing Sam. Even though we knew he was happy with Sarah and Joe, sometimes we wished he could live with us.

Right away, Sarah and Joe sent pictures. They also called every Thursday night to tell us all the new things Sam was doing.

Joe told us, "He laughs when we kiss him."

Sarah said, "His favorite song is *De Colores*."

After that phone call, Mommy began singing again.

On the Saturday after Kindergarten ended, we visited Sam at Joe and Sarah's house. Sam was big and could almost sit up!

When I sang *De Colores*, he smiled and made noises like he was singing too. When I made silly faces, he reached for me.

I read Sam his books and helped him play with his toys.

Sam has a big crib and lots of toys but I didn't see a stroller. I asked Joe, "Do you have a nice stroller to push Sam in?"

"You're a good sister to think about that," Joe said. He took me out to the garage and showed it to me.

After seeing Sam, we all felt very happy.

Now we visit Sam lots. We talk to Joe and Sarah on the phone and share letters and pictures.

Sometimes, I miss Sam. Then I need to talk to Mommy or draw in my Sam coloring book. But I know Sam is where he should be. And even though he doesn't live with Mommy and me, we will always be part of his family.

Because, when I was five, something very special happened…

I became Sam's Sister.

De Colores, Spanish lyrics

De Colores
De Colores se visten los campos
    en la primavera
De Colores
De Colores son los pajarillos que vienen
    de afuera
De Colores
De Colores es el arco iris que
vemos lucir

Y por eso los grandes amores
De muchos colores
Me Gustan a mi
Y por eso los grandes amores
De muchos colores
Me Gustan a mi

Canta el gallo
Canta el gallo con el quiri quiri quiri quiri quiri
La gallina
La gallina con el cara cara cara cara cara
Los polluelos
Los polluelos con el pio pio pio pio pi

Y por eso los grandes amores De Colores
De muchos colores
Me Gustan a mi
Y por eso los grandes amores
De muchos colores
Me Gustan a mi

De Colores, *English lyrics*

Move your arms like a flying bird

In colors
The fields dress themselves in all
   colors for us in the springtime
In colors
Little birds arrive from afar in all colors
In colors
The rainbow lights up in bright colors for
   us all to see

Open your arms wide to show the rainbow.

Cross your arms. Open your arms. Put your hand to your heart. Again open your arms. Put your hand to your heart.

And it is all these great loves
of the many bright colors
that brings joy and sunshine to me
And it is all these great loves
of the many bright colors
that brings joy and sunshine to me

Sings the rooster
Sings the rooster with his kiri kiri kiri kiri kiri
And the cluck hen with her cara cara cara
   cara cara

Choose someone to sing like the rooster, someone else to sing like the hen, and others to be the little chicks.

And the baby chicks
And the baby chicks with their pio pio
   pio pio pi

And it is all these great loves
of the many bright colors
that brings joy and sunshine to me
And it is all these great loves
of the many bright colors
that brings joy and sunshine to me

Translation from Spanish to English by Erica Brooke Johnston

About the Publisher

Perspectives Press, Inc.
The Infertility and Adoption Publisher

Since 1982 Perspectives Press, Inc. has focused exclusively on infertility, adoption, and related reproductive health and child welfare issues. Our purpose is to promote understanding of these issues and to educate and sensitize those personally experiencing these life situations, professionals who work in these fields, and the public at large. Our titles are never duplicative or competitive with material already available through other publishers. We seek to find and to fill niches which are empty.

Please see our website for a list of currently in print titles.
www.perspectivespress.com

About the Author

Juliet C. Bond, LCSW has been working in the foster care and adoption field for over 10 years. She attributes her professional dedication to children and families to the life lessons and unconditional love her own beautiful children and husband have afforded her. Currently, she provides counseling and support to birthparents at The Cradle, in Evanston, Illinois, one of the country's oldest and most respected adoption agencies. Juliet wrote *Sam's Sister* after seeing several birthmothers abandon their adoption plans due to anxiety around revealing their decision to the children they were already parenting. During her research, Juliet discovered that over 60% of birthmothers were parenting other children at the time of placement! She was particularly interested in providing avenues for children to deal with grief and loss around having a sibling adopted. Juliet felt, with better tools, birthmothers and their children might feel more confident and comfortable in making their adoption plans. She hopes this book affords comfort and peace to families making such an important life decision.

About the Illustrator

A New Castle, Delaware resident along with her husband and son, Dawn W. Majewski earned a Bachelor of Fine Arts degree in illustration from The Moore College of Art in Philadelphia, PA after having lived the often-moving experience of being part of a U. S. Army career officer's family. Since graduating from Moore College her art has gone through the fields of graphic design, illustration, instructing, and fine art principally in watercolor and pastel painting. As a freelance artist, in addition to her employment as an artist by businesses, schools, and colleges in the Philadelphia area, Dawn has had many private clients for whom she has done wall graphics, portraiture, and book illustration among other art venues. In a related area, Dawn writes poetry and was runner up as Bucks County (PA) Poet Laureate and in the national Robert Fraser Open Poetry Competition.